Going to the Dentis.

Sheila Hollins, Amber Qureshi and Lloyd Page
illustrated by Beth Webb

Beyond Words

London

10

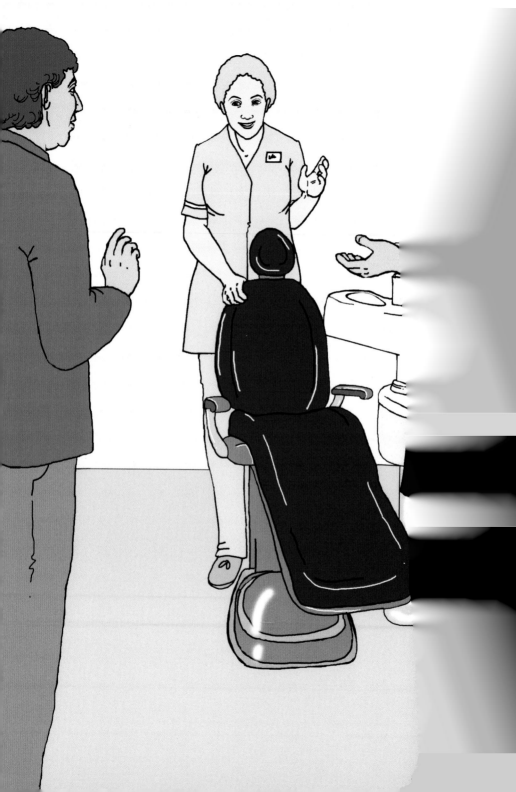

12

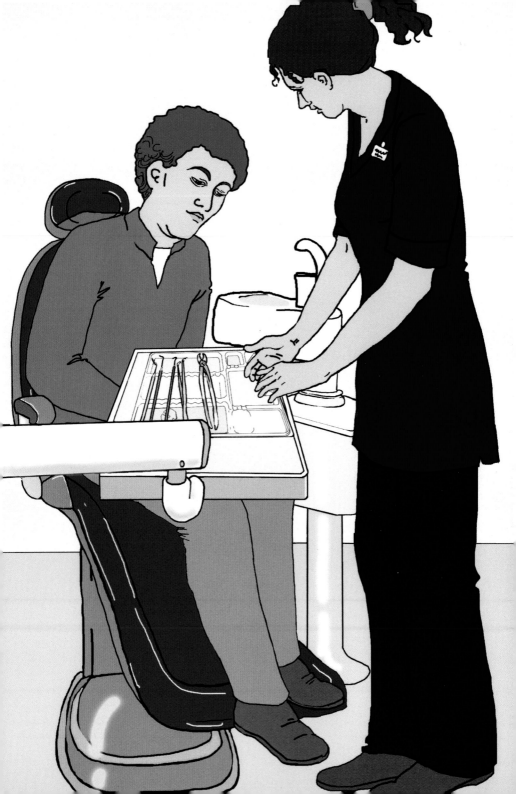

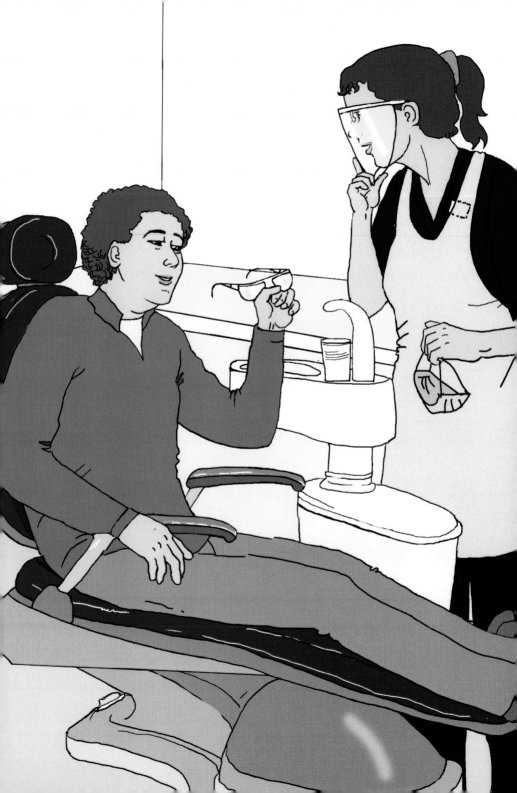

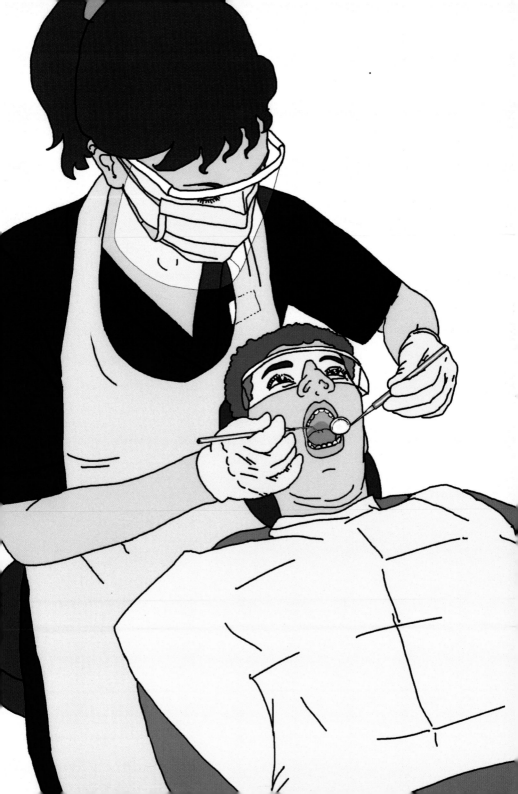

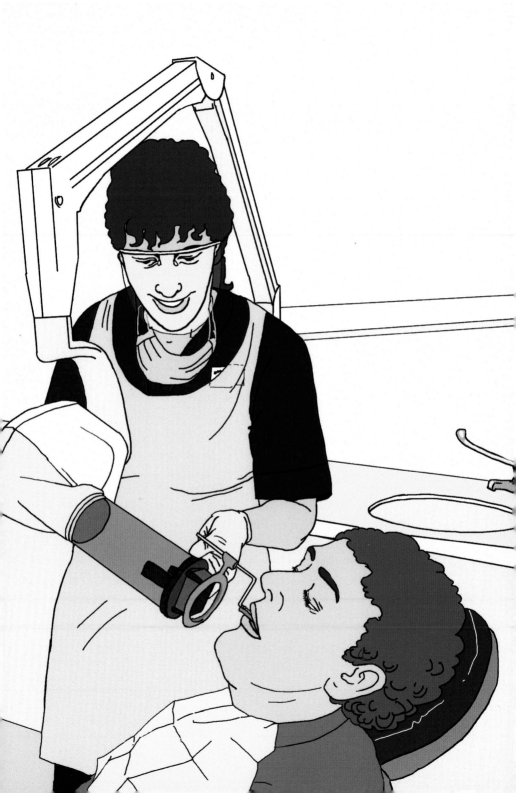

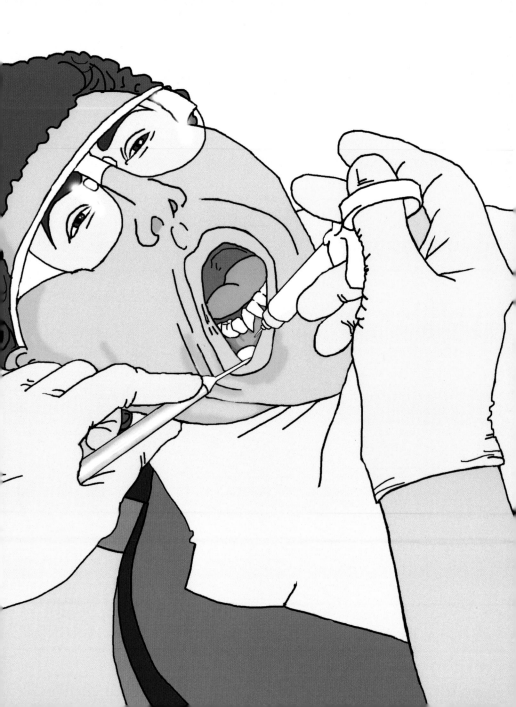

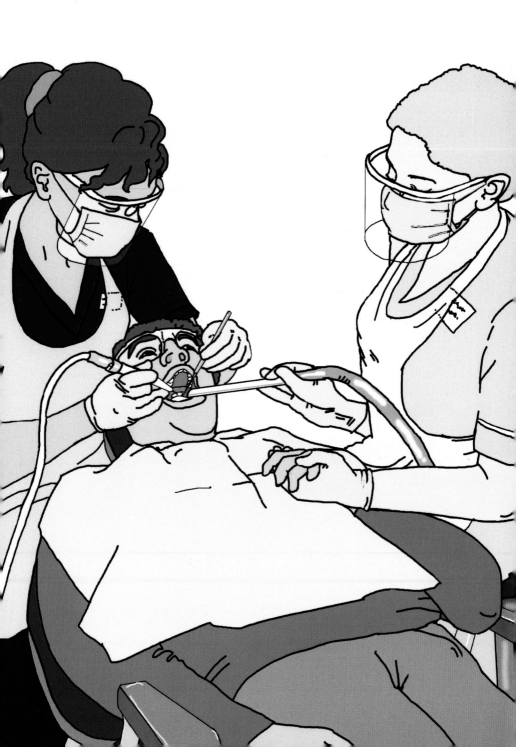

23

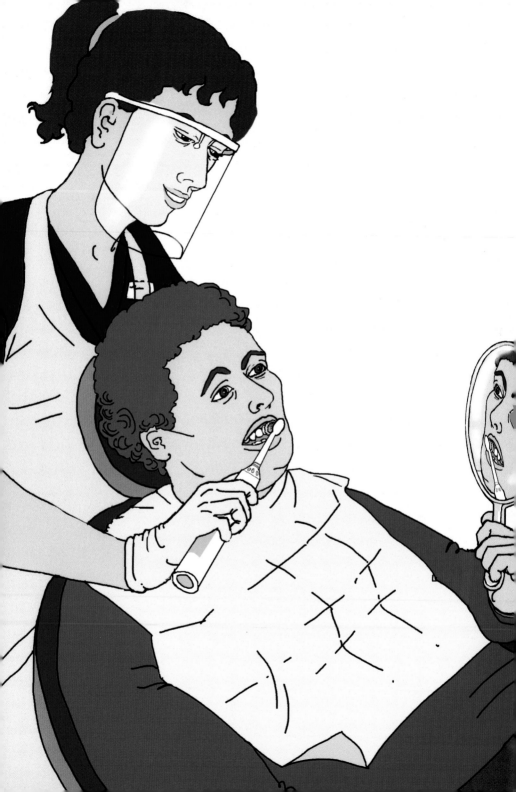

First published in the UK 2016 by Books Beyond Words, charity number 1183942 (England and Wales).

Text & illustrations © Books Beyond Words, 2016.

ISBN 978-1-78458-084-1

British Library Cataloguing-in-Publication Data

A catalogue record for this book is available from the British Library.

Printed by Royal British Legion Industries, Leatherhead.

Further information about the Books Beyond Words series can be obtained from our website: www.booksbeyondwords.co.uk.

Contents

Storyline

The following words are provided for readers and supporters who want some ideas about one possible story. Most readers make their own story up from the pictures.

1. Matthew shops at the supermarket. He buys lots of sugary food and drink.

2. Matthew has cake and cola and watches TV.

3. Matthew can't sleep. His tooth hurts.

4. In the morning, Matthew tells Mum his tooth hurts.

5. Mum knows a nice dentist. She makes an appointment for Matthew.

6. Matthew talks to the receptionist at the dentist's surgery.

7. The receptionist gives Matthew some forms and a copy of this book. Matthew feels nervous.

8. Matthew reads this book with Mum. He feels a bit better.

9. The dentist meets Matthew in the waiting room. She is very friendly.

10. The dentist shows Matthew into the treatment room. He says hello to the dental nurse.

11. Matthew sits in the dentist's chair.

12. The dentist shows Matthew some of the tools she uses.

13. Matthew can say yes to let the dentist look at his teeth or he can say no. He thinks about it.

14. Matthew decides to let the dentist look at his teeth. She gives him some glasses to wear to protect his eyes.

15. The dentist moves the chair. Now Matthew is lying down. Matthew opens his mouth wide. The dentist checks his teeth.

16. The dentist explains to Matthew that she wants to x-ray his teeth. Matthew can decide whether to have the x-ray or not.

17. The dentist points the x-ray machine at Matthew's mouth. Matthew bites down on a piece of plastic.

18. The dentist stands outside the room and presses the x-ray button. Mum waits outside too. Matthew keeps very still for the x-ray. It doesn't hurt.

19. Matthew and Mum look at his x-ray with the dentist. She shows Matthew that he has a cavity (a hole) in one of his teeth. He needs a filling.

20. The dentist explains to Matthew about having a filling. They look at a picture of an injection.

21. The injection hurts a bit but it's over quickly. It makes his mouth go numb.

22. The dentist uses her tools to do the filling. The dental nurse holds Matthew's hand. He can squeeze her hand if he wants the dentist to stop.

23. Matthew rinses out his mouth with mouthwash. He dribbles because his mouth is still numb.

24. Matthew looks at his teeth in a mirror.

25. He says thank you and goodbye to the dentist. He feels happy it's all over.

26. Matthew and Mum go home. Monty is happy to see them.

27. Matthew feeds Monty.

28. Matthew sleeps well. His toothache is gone.

29. Matthew and Mum go back to the dentist.

30. Matthew sits in the dentist's chair. He feels relaxed.

31. The dentist shows Matthew how to clean his teeth. She uses an electric toothbrush.

32. Matthew practises brushing his teeth.

33. Matthew reads some leaflets. One is about looking after your teeth. One is about eating the right food.

34. Matthew shops at the supermarket. He buys healthy foods without lots of sugar.

35. Matthew eats an apple after his dinner.

36. Matthew reads this book about going to the dentist. Monty sits with him.

37. Matthew brushes his teeth with an electric toothbrush before bed. He has mouthwash too.

38. Matthew says goodnight to Monty.

39. Matthew takes good care of his teeth. Everyone can see Matthew's clean and healthy teeth when he smiles.

Information for dental health professionals

Communication methods

Good communication is vital in every aspect of life but more so in situations where people are anxious, uncertain, fearful and possibly in pain. Communication needs to be clear, direct and simple, and some general rules of thumb are included below.

Communication within the dental team

- Do place appropriate alerts on notes. For example, how a particular individual behaves when feeling anxious.

- Do ask the supporter and inform the nurse, in advance if possible, of any things which might help to make the individual feel more at ease and treatment more successful. For example, a person may feel comforted by holding the nurse's hand or twisting paper for reassurance.

- Do ensure the entire dental team is able to use a variety of communication styles and approaches (augmentative and alternative communication, AAC) such as:
  - this book – Going to the Dentist
  - gestures and body language
  - sign language
  - objects of reference
  - drawings, symbols, photographs and videos
  - technology, e.g. using tablets with adjustable viewing size for people with a visual impairment.

45

Communicating with the patient and supporter

- Use the most appropriate method of communication for each person.

- Talk to the individual but don't talk down.

- Allow time for the person to process your question before repeating it or asking another.

- Make eye contact as you would with all patients, unless the patient avoids eye gaze.

- Speak clearly and slowly with simple words and short sentences.

- Check for understanding by asking them to explain what they have understood.

Capacity assessments for informed consent

In England and Wales the person is assumed to have decision-making capacity. It is the dental professional's responsibility to do a mental capacity assessment if there is any doubt.

A mental capacity assessment determines whether an individual:

1. can understand relevant information pertaining to each specific decision about dental treatment;

2. can retain that information;

3. can weigh up the pros and cons of that information to arrive at a decision;

4. can communicate that decision to you in words, signs, pictures or behaviour.

If you think that an individual lacks capacity or you are uncertain, first check whether it is just an 'off' day and the person is feeling unwell. If so, reschedule the appointment. You could also consider referral to a special care dental service. If you remain concerned about the person's capacity to make a decision, then a best interest meeting with people who know the patient well is necessary.

Reasonable adjustments

There are many simple steps that can be taken to encourage dental attendance, taking into consideration the needs of both supporters and patients.

- Try to schedule appointments so that the timings are optimal, for example early mornings may be difficult for supporters and patients.

- Try to see anxious people on time so that they are not kept waiting unnecessarily. It may be a good idea to schedule appointments first thing after lunch.

- If possible, shorten the duration of appointments so that individuals can cope comfortably.

- Wear a transparent full face visor, rather than a face mask so that patients can see your smile and read your lips if necessary.

- Explain each stage of the treatment in short sentences with no jargon.

- Do not move the dental chair without first informing the person.

- Use topical anaesthesia; your patients will appreciate it!

- Provide a distraction, such as pictures on the ceiling.

- Play relaxing background music or allow the patient to wear headphones, especially during drilling.

- Encourage the person's accompanying supporter to stay with them if that helps.

Time taken to build a solid foundation of trust is priceless and will reap dividends for future dental care. An initial familiarisation visit will help to build confidence. In an urgent situation or when confidence building and anxiety reduction has not been possible there are a range of treatment possibilities:

1. behaviour management – non-pharmacological (for example desensitisation where a person is slowly introduced to various aspects of a dental visit) and/or pharmacological (where a patient is prescribed medicine to relax them the night before an appointment)

2. inhalational sedation

3. intravenous sedation

4. general anaesthesia.

General tips

Although appointments and patients are part of your daily routine, for some people, a dental visit will have a big impact and leave a lasting impression on them, so always make sure you smile and:

- recognise that each person is an individual;

48

- learn about the support needs that are typical for a person with this condition;

- read the notes before seeing the person and take special note of any advice given by family carers;

- understand how the person usually behaves when anxious.

Information for supporters and carers

Communication

Good communication is key. There are many useful pieces of information you can give the dental team to contribute to a successful appointment.

Up-to-date and complete medical information is necessary to carry out dental treatment safely. Please do give the dental team all available medical information even if you think it may have no connection to dental treatment. The mouth is a part of the body and sometimes it's surprising how another condition or medication can affect a person. Below are some more things you can do.

- Bring an up-to-date list of medication and details of any recent or relevant hospital admissions/ appointments.

- Inform the dental team of what to expect when the individual is anxious, for example some people might run away when they are anxious.

- Bring an item which may add reassurance, e.g. a favourite object, item of clothing or MP3 player.

- Do not be afraid to ask questions or raise concerns.

Consent

The dentist will not start any treatment without first giving an explanation. As is the case with all health professionals, dentists will not undertake any treatment on anyone without first seeking informed consent. Consent can be verbal and/or written and involves understanding what is involved in carrying out treatment(s), the various options available, and likely outcomes. This means that the dentist will explain what will happen, for example in a check-up. The dentist will explain the risks and benefits of the various options that are available, before agreeing the treatment plan. Please be reassured that:

- dentists treat everyone as an individual;

- dentists recognise that an individual has the right to participate in decisions about dental treatment.

General tips

If you are supporting someone with complex needs or someone who has a heightened sensitivity to touch or sound, such as a person with autism, you might prefer to find a special care dentist. Your GP can organise a referral to a special care service. Alternatively, in the UK, the General Dental Council (GDC) has a database of all registered special care dentists which you can search on their website to find your nearest service. See 'Useful resources' for more information.

Remember, dentists enter the profession of dentistry to help relieve others of pain. Below are some ways you can help.

- Do not tell any dental 'horror stories' prior to the appointment.

- Make the evening and night before the appointment as stress free as possible.

- Try to make sure the patient has enough sleep the night before.

- On the day of the appointment, make sure both you and the patient are feeling as positive as you can.

- If you are frightened of the dentist, try not to transfer your fear to the person who is the patient.

Looking after our teeth and gums

As well as visiting the dentist regularly, it is very important that we take proper care of our teeth at home, in between visits.

Cleaning our teeth stops plaque from building up so we are less likely to get cavities (holes) in our teeth and gum disease. Everyone should brush their teeth at least twice a day with fluoride toothpaste: once in the morning and once in the evening before going to bed.

Lots of dentists recommend electric toothbrushes because they can make it easier to clean the teeth at the back of the mouth. Of course an electric toothbrush won't be suitable for everyone and there are lots of different manual ones to choose from. There are also lots of specialist brushes and grips available for people who find a regular toothbrush hard to hold. Your dentist can give advice on choosing the right toothbrush.

It is also a good idea to use floss or interdental brushes to clean in between teeth. After brushing, rinsing with a fluoride mouthwash will get rid of any last bits of food or bacteria that might still be in the mouth. Always spit out mouthwash, don't swallow it.

Our diet plays a big part in how healthy our teeth and gums are. We should all try to avoid eating and drinking lots of sugary things and limit any sugary food and drink to mealtimes. Sugar creates acid in our mouths that eats away at the enamel (the outside layer) of our teeth. This leads to cavities (holes) forming in our teeth which can cause pain and infection and will require dental treatment.

Between meals it is best to drink water rather than fizzy drinks or fruit juices that contain lots of sugar. Also try to avoid snacking between mealtimes or at least stick to snacks like nuts, cheese or raw vegetables. It is a really good idea to rinse your mouth after eating.

Some medical words explained

Local anaesthetic: Before you have any treatment the dentist will give you a special medicine called an anaesthetic. This medicine will make your mouth go numb so that the treatment doesn't hurt you. Sometimes it's given through an injection and sometimes by rubbing on a gel.

Appointment: The date and time when people have to see the dentist. The dentist's surgery sends people appointment cards or letters. These tell them what day and time they need to be there. You should tell the dentist's surgery if you need any special adjustments to the time, for example if you need the first or last appointment, or a longer appointment.

Cavity: A hole in your tooth.

Check-up: A regular appointment where your dentist can check that all parts of your teeth, gums and mouth are healthy. Your dentist will tell you how often you need a check-up.

Decay: Cavities (holes) in your teeth and rotten teeth are types of tooth decay.

Dental nurse: They are trained to help the dentist and to help patients feel more comfortable. They wear a different uniform to the dentist.

Dentist: A type of doctor for your teeth.

Enamel: The hard, outside layer on your teeth. Brushing your teeth helps to protect the enamel.

Floss: Very thin string that you use to clean between your teeth.

Filling: When the dentist repairs a cavity (a hole) in one of your teeth they will fill the hole with a tooth coloured or metal paste that hardens.

Gums: The pink skin around your teeth. You should clean the areas where your gums meet your teeth (as well as the different sides of each of your teeth) to keep them healthy and stop gum disease.

Mouthwash: A liquid to rinse your mouth with to get rid of the germs in your mouth. It usually tastes minty.

Plaque: A sticky coating that builds up on your teeth. Plaque can lead to tooth decay and gum disease. It is important to brush your teeth and clean around your gums to get rid of plaque.

Toothache and **mouth pain**: You should go to see your dentist if your teeth or gums hurt, or if any part of your mouth feels or looks strange. The dentist can check your teeth, gums and mouth to see why it hurts.

X-ray: This is a type of photograph that can see the bones and teeth inside your mouth. When the x-ray is taken you must keep still.

Useful resources

Services in the UK

British Society of Paediatric Dentistry (BSPD)
The national society dedicated to improving the oral health of children from birth to 16.
www.bspd.co.uk

General Dental Council (GDC)
The GDC register qualified dental professionals, set and enforce standards of dental practice and conduct, protect the public from illegal practice and investigate complaints. The GDC hold lists of all registered dentists and dental care professionals in the UK which you can search on their website.
www.gdc-uk.org

They have created an easy read guide to explain who they are and what they do.
www.gdc-uk.org/Newsandpublications/Publications/Publications/Smile%20EasyRead.pdf

British Society for Disability and Oral Health (BSDH)
The BSDH exists to promote the oral health of people with disabilities of all ages. This includes raising awareness of the barriers to accessing oral health care for patients with disabilities. Their website offers information for both patients and professionals.
www.bsdh.org

BDA Smile
The independent dental advice website for patients by the **British Dental Association (BDA)**.
www.bdasmile.org

British Dental Health Foundation
An independent dental charity working to improve standards of oral health and hygiene in the UK and worldwide.
www.dentalhealth.org

Written materials available on the internet

Easy Health
This accessible information website has links to lots of leaflets and videos about how to keep your teeth and gums healthy.
www.easyhealth.org.uk

Delivering better oral health: an evidence-based toolkit for prevention. Produced by **Public Health England**, this toolkit provides practical, evidence-based guidance to help clinical teams promote good oral health in their patients.
www.gov.uk/government/publications/delivering-better-oral-health-an-evidence-based-toolkit-for-prevention

Healthy Smiles for Autism: Oral Hygiene Tips for Children with Autistic Spectrum Disorder, produced by the **National Museum of Dentistry** (University of Maryland, US), is a best practices guide to oral health care for children with ASD.
www.dental.umaryland.edu/museum/index.html/resources/healthy-smiles-for-autism/

Oral Health Care for People with Profound and Multiple Learning Disabilities. Produced by **Pamis**, this leaflet explains the oral health problems people with PMLD

are more likely to experience and gives guidance on how best to maintain good oral health.
http://pamis.org.uk/cms/files/leaflets/oral_health_leaflet.pdf

"How to Brush Your Teeth with an Electric Powered Toothbrush" provides step-by-step instructions, illustrated with photographs, on how to brush your teeth effectively when using an electric toothbrush.
www.freysmiles.com/blog/view/how-to-brush-your-teeth-with-an-electric-powered-toothbrush

Videos

"How to use an electric toothbrush – AJ Hedger" is an instructional video, created by AJ Hedger & Associates (a dental practice), which you can watch for free on YouTube.
www.youtube.com/watch?v=L3SllxdLGxl

Related titles

Going to the Doctor (1996) by Sheila Hollins, Jane Bernal and Matthew Gregory, illustrated by Beth Webb. This book illustrates a variety of experiences which may occur during a visit to the GP. These include meeting the doctor, having one's ears syringed, a physical examination, a blood test, a blood pressure check and getting a prescription.

Going into Hospital (2015, 2nd edition) by Sheila Hollins, Angie Avis and Samantha Cheverton, with Jim Blair, illustrated by Denise Redmond. This book helps to prepare and support people for planned or emergency hospital admissions.

Going to Out-Patients (2009, 2nd edition) by Sheila Hollins, Jane Bernal and Matthew Gregory, illustrated by Denise Redmond. This book explains what happens in out-patient departments, covering tests such as ultrasound, x-ray and hearing tests. Feelings, information and consent to treatment are addressed.

George Gets Smart (2001) by Sheila Hollins, Margaret Flynn and Philippa Russell, illustrated by Catherine Brighton. George's life changes when he learns how to keep clean and smart. People no longer avoid being with him and he enjoys the company of his work mates and friends.

Rose Gets in Shape (2016) by Roger Banks and Paul Wallang, illustrated by Mike Nicholson. Rose lives on her own and she has picked up some bad habits about eating and taking exercise. Her energy is low and she gets tired easily. When her doctor tells her that her weight is causing health problems she decides to get in shape. We follow Rose through the

60

struggles and triumphs of her weight loss journey, the new activities she takes up, and the good friends and support she finds along the way.

See www.booksbeyondwords.co.uk for the full range of titles.

Authors and artist

Sheila Hollins is Emeritus Professor of Psychiatry of Disability at St George's, University of London, and sits in the House of Lords. She is a past President of the Royal College of Psychiatrists and of the BMA. She is the founder, lead editor and Executive Chair for Books Beyond Words, and a family carer.

Dr Amber Qureshi, MBA, is a specialist in special care dentistry with nearly two decades of experience working in the NHS. She has recently added psychology to her postgraduate portfolio and she is passionate about improving oral health and raising awareness of mouth cancer. Currently, she works in a consultancy capacity.

Lloyd Page has worked as an adviser for Beyond Words for many years. Lloyd volunteers at Mencap and is part of the learning disability panel and a Mencap spokesperson for health. He is a campaigner for Changing Places and has been involved in the Olympic and Paralympic Games.

Beth Webb is the artist who helped to develop the concept of Books Beyond Words in its early days. She is also the author of 14 novels for children and young people and is a professional storyteller.

Acknowledgments

We are grateful for the advice and support of our advisory group, which included representatives from Southern Health NHS Foundation Trust, Great Ormond Street Hospital, Virgin Care, King's College London Department of Special Care Dentistry, Bromley Sparks, Somerset Partnership NHS Trust, Guys and St Thomas's NHS Trust, Central and North-West London NHS Foundation Trust and Haringey Community Dental Services: Raj Attavar, Jayne Jazz, Kym Anderson, Carol Mason, Selina Master, Ivana Radenovic, Teresa Durman, Linda Allchorne, Kamala Chelliah, Nigel Hollins, Paddy Finnegan, Mary Burke, Bernice Knight, Kerry Brathwaite, Nicky Sharples and Rosemary Achieng Akaighe.

We are also grateful to all the people who read earlier drafts of the picture story, including groups from Plymouth People First: Plymouth Highbury Trust, The Vine, Michael Batt Foundation and Pluss; Virgin Care special care dentistry patients; staff from King's College Hospital; staff from Mencap; clients and staff of the Buckinghamshire learning disability service; Bromley Sparks; Watford and Wimbledon Libraries' Beyond Words book clubs and Peninsula Dental Social Enterprise.

We are grateful to the Tangley Trust and Southern Health NHS Foundation Trust for their generous funding of this book.